{ MADAME M PRESENTS }

# CREEPY
# LITTLE
# BEDTIME
# STORIES

{ MADAME M PRESENTS }

# CREEPY LITTLE BEDTIME STORIES

creepy little productions

Phoenix, Arizona

Published by Creepy Little Productions
Phoenix, Arizona

Creepy Little Productions, #327
3535 West Dunlap Ave.
Phoenix, Arizona 85051

Library of Congress Card Number: 00-191984

ISBN 0-9704159-0-7

Printed in the United States of America

First Edition

Cover, Interior Design and Illustrations by Christy A. Moeller-Masel
Poetry by Christy A. Moeller-Masel

Special Thanks to: Joe Masel, Kelly Scott, Sharon Moeller and Nichole Ross for their loving support of this book.

VISIT OUR WEBSITE AT
www.creepylittlestories.com

For Joe

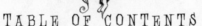

# TABLE OF CONTENTS

# MADAME M

Hello, My Dahlings
I am Madame M
Mistress of The Creepy Things
That cause the mayhem

I'm not easily pleased
Like a Holly Homemaker
Some say I'm mysterious
So to speak, "Widowmaker"

Using quill for my pen
To write tainted word
Although, on occasion
They may sound absurd

All of these tales
Spun with spider webs
May make little angels
Not sleep in their beds

And this batch, freshly brewed
With wild creature stories,
Tells of monsters and ghoulies
That give children worries

Like dear Witchy-Boo
Who used a magic spell
To take away warts
And make her a bombshell

Stories of Girls
with troublesome heads
And bad little boys
Who won't go to bed

Naughty creatures and outcasts
In words, I have found,
When read in the dark
From these pages they'll bound

DANGER, Heed this warning
Not for faint of heart
For a coward or dullard
These pages won't part

And take all in stride
'Tis an immortal's tale
This book has bewitched you
Now you're under it's spell!

# LIL' SPIDER GIRL

Here's a little story
About a girl I know.
Her name is Lil' Spider Girl,
And she's a Black Widow

Her hair is made of cobwebs,
Her legs are long and thin
And when I start to counting,
She has four too many limbs

Her lips are small and rosy red
They match her little fangs,
She smells so sweet, a scent they call,
"Ode De Toilette Wolfbanes"

So don't be afraid if you see her
With her face so ghostly white,
Just don't accept her offer,
To go out to have a bite

# THE BAT BOY

Underneath a bridge
In the middle of the city,
Hangs an awkward creature
Who laughs like he's giddy

With a dark velvet cape
He's an ominous sight,
He glides through the sky
In the middle of the night

Wind blows through his hair-
A shiny, black Pompadour-
When he flies off to work
As an Elvis impersonator

He goes by Bat Boy
His real name is Vlad,
But don't call him that
It'll just make him mad

# THE TWO-FACED GIRL

I once met a girl
That had two faces
She'd been in a circus
And traveled many places

Two heads and one body
She was quite an odd sight
The first time I saw her
I nearly fainted in fright

Both mouths spoke together
When I asked her her name
"I'm Duo" - "I'm Donna"
A really great dame

I took her out for dinner
All-you-can-eat and then some
She stuffed her faces for hours
But I paid for just one

But the strangest thing about her
Was not her four tiny ears
But when one looked at the other
She resembled Shakespeare

(Squint your eyes and take another look)

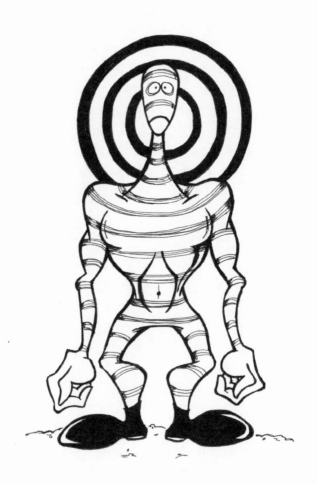

# TARGET MAN

Target Man lives
In the desert in Nevada
Where it gets very hot
And it's just getting hotta

He worked in Las Vegas
As a knife thrower's assistant
Until he retired after
A freak side show incident

Now he works for
The U.S. Government
On a missile-testing site
Nuclear experiment

He works hard at his job
And really likes to try
But, the missile-testing planes
Use him for the bullseye

# WITCHY BOO-BOO

When Witchy Boo-Boo was
Just a young ghoul
Her mother would tell her
To "Follow One Rule"

"Never use witchcraft
For personal gain
It'll only cause heartache
And worst of all... PAIN"

Many years later
When her powers were stronger
Boo-Boo thought
She'd like her legs longer

"And then, while I'm at it
I'll get rid of this fat"
She patted her tummy
"Most guys don't like that"

"And this wart on my face
It too has to go
And my chest is too small
I will make it grow"

13

So, with an "Abracadabra"
And a flick of her wand
Her short, squatty legs
Began to elong

The fat in her tummy
Began to erase
And the legs she had wished for
Took over it's place

The wart that she wanted
Gone, as she said,
Became a big ugly
Hole in her head

And her small petite chest
Grew out of distortions
They grew and they grew
To enormous proportions

They blew up for a while
Like balloons that are bloated
Till they just got so large
They up and exploded

As Witchy Boo-Boo laid
All mangled, she thought
"I should've just listened
To what my mom taught"

# ONE DAY UNTIL HALLOWEEN

One day until Halloween
The final countdown
And I needed a costume
To scare the whole town

I don't want something goofy,
Or silly or funny
I won't dress like a clown
Or a white Easter Bunny

No knight in armor
from a dull fairy story
I want something gruesome
And spooky and gory

I walked into a costume shop,
The only one in town
It used to be a cemetery
Before they tore it down

They had tons of disguises
Like a vampire cape
And a two-headed zombie
And a giant green ape

And many rubber masks
In all sizes and styles
The rack they sat on
Went for miles and miles

Monsters and demons
And a vampire vixen
They even had a mask
That looked like Richard Nixon

But the scariest costume
More than the Grim Reaper
Was the one that was worn
By the lonely shopkeeper

His clothes were all torn
They were the wrong size
And out of the rips
Were tiny red eyes

His shoes made a noise
Like a rattle would make
Because they were made
Of live rattlesnake

His face was thin and pale
You would think he was dead
And two big bulgy eyes
Popped out of his head

They were each different sizes
One red and one yellow
And the wart on his nose
Made this one ugly fellow

I walked to the counter
"That's the costume for me,
The one you have on
Is what I want to be."

"It's gruesome! It's gory!
It's absolutely horrific!
I simply must have it!
I think it's terrific."

"I love how your mask
Is so slimy, it's groovy
It's just like a monster
From a late night scary movie."

"And the bugs that are crawling
On your head look so real
It certainly has a frightening
Creepy kind of appeal."

"So, how much to look
Like I've crawled from a tomb?
How much to buy
Your disgusting costume?"

He sat in long silence
As if comatose
I watched his skin peel
It was really quite gross

He slowly leaned over
And closed his small eye
He stared at me crossly,
I wanted to die

He tapped his long fingers
And looked 'round the room,
As he said, "Sorry, Sonny,
I don't wear a costume"

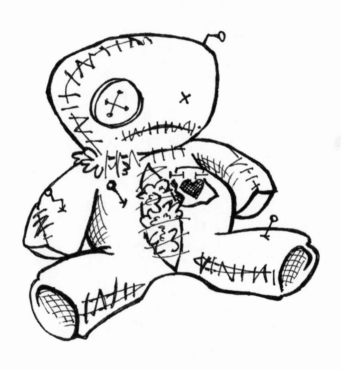

# VOODOO DOLL

With a pin through his heart
And his mouth sewn shut
Buttons for eyes
And moss padding his butt

Dear Voodoo Doll sits
In the same happy pose.
He knows how to cause things
Nobody else knows

With a stick of a pin
He controls all your aches
With a spark from a flame
Your heartburn he makes

You'll suffer if he falls
Or jumps off the shelf
But if it makes you feel better,
He also hurts himself...

# JOHNNY IS A ROCK STAR

Johnny's been a rock star
Ever since birth
They announced his arrival
All over the Earth

He was born with a microphone
Sticking out of his mouth
And cried with a drawl
Like they have in the South

He smiles so bright
It stretches ear to ear
They could see it shining
From the Space Station MIR

They knew when they saw
He was born with sideburns,
Girls cheered in the streets,
"The King returns!"

But as soon as the cheers
Leapt out of their lips
The nurses all noticed
He was born with no hips!

What kind of a rock star
Can't shake, rattle and roll?
Why, without swingin' hips,
He dances quite dull

So the doctors came up
With a nifty new plan
They would give this boy hips
However they can

They set a date
For the operation
And the news announced
Their Special Presentation!

"Live tonight!
On this station!
Johnny's hip transplant
Operation!"

Everyone watched
That night on the tellie,
Would Johnny make it?
Well, will he?

(News Reporter)
"We're here in the hospital
This Friday night
Coming to you live
Via satellite!"

"The doctors give Johnny
a 50/50 chance
As to whether or not
He will ever dance."

"Dr. Bamboozall,
Answer me with conviction,
What will you do
For his anti-hip condition?"

(Dr. Bamboozall)
"Ve've received a donor,
Who's recently passed on
He vent by ze name
Of 'Ol Dancin' Don'"

"He'z a Disco King
From '74 or '75
And just vants his dancin'
To be Stayin' Alive"

After 24 hours,
At a quarter to one,
The doctors announced
"Ze operation iz done!"

"I'm pleased to zay
Everything vent quite swell
As to vhether it vorked
I'll let Johnny tell"

The doors opened slowly
The crowd went quiet
The news cameras got closer
This was the highlight!

Johnny came out swingin'
His new, hippy tushie
The girl all went crazy
And their legs went mushy.

The crowd was wild
For the protege' they had found
And Johnny, Rock's King,
was finally crowned

# THE HEADLESS GIRL

As I walked
The other day
My head fell off
And rolled away

I tried to chase it
Down the street
But it rolled
Beneath my feet

I tripped and fell
Flat on my neck
I'm sure I looked like
Quite a wreck

I wondered what
My mom would say
When she found my head
Had gotten away

(She'd say:)
"I always told you,
As a matter of fact,
You'd lose you head
If it wasn't attached!"

To avoid Mom's wrath
Which was my fate
I decided a new face
Is what I would create

I popped off a head
From my favorite fashion doll
And attached it on my neck
Tho' it was too small

Then I tied a pretty ribbon
Around my little neck
But still my mother noticed
"Oh geez, oh shoot, oh heck!"

She went and found my old head
Hiding underneath the tree
It was as scared as I was
It knew how Mom can be.

She sewed it back on top of me
With nylon fishing tackle
And filled in all the gaps
With Extra Strength Brand spackle

She put on a thick layer
Of new improved white glue
And added a strip of
Silver duck tape (or two)

But, still my head
Had a mind of it's own
And would disappear at night
To places unknown

Till one night I decided
To just enjoy my head
And left my lazy body
Back asleep in bed

Where I ended up,
I was sure surprised
At a local night club
Looking at familiar eyes

I found split personalities
Must be quite contagious
'Cuz everybody dancing there
Was half there and outrageous

You wouldn't think
You'd have great parties
When the everybodies
Don't have bodies!

But now I make sure
On those Friday nights
To be there dancing
'Neath the disco lights

Shaking and bouncing
Like a big round beach ball
It's about what's in your head,
Not your body at all!

# WOLFMAN JOE

One day Joe discovered
Something odd about his face
There were patches of fur
All over the place

Long whiskers he'd comb
But they wouldn't behave
Joe thought, "Well, maybe
I just need a shave."

So he moseyed on down
To the local barber shop
He passed by the striped pole
With the gold ball on top

The barber lathered Joe up
With Burma shaving cream
And shaved him until
His face was soft and clean

But it quickly grew back
Ten fold it did seem
So they lathered him up
With more shaving cream

As the years went by
Joe just couldn't keep up
And he started to look
Like a pure bred wolf pup

He grew a small tail
And a great pair of fangs
His hair got real knotted
And he suffered from mange

He felt oddly strange
When there was a full moon
He barked and he howled
And he would start to croon

His neighbors would yell
"Hey look! It's Wolf Boy!"
The mean kids would call him
"That ugly stuffed toy"

It was hard for ol' Joe
To be so big and hairy
He wanted to be liked
Not thought of as scary

Then one day while Joe
Was playing Throw and Fetcher'
He got caught in the net
Of the local dog catcher

Back at the pound
Joe pleaded his case
"I'm just a man,
With a real hairy face!"

The vets all prodded
And poked him with sticks
X-rayed his insides
And dissected his ticks

They finally came to
An enormous conclusion
This wolf was a man
Needing a blood transfusion

The nurses stuck in
A huge honkin' IV
They asked him real gently
"Sir, coffee or tea?"

He said, "Gimme coffee!
A Columbian blend
Pump me full of java
Percolate to the end!"

After two cups of coffee
Joe's hair did recede
Doctor screamed "It's the coffee!
With Espresso proceed!"

They injected all kinds
of beans-roasted and fired
Sumatra and Jamaican
Until Joe was wired

They ran the IV
from morning till night
Till the doctor exclaimed
"Now, this boy's alright!"

"My job here is done
The cause, now you know
All you were needing
Was a stiff cup of Joe."

# MONSTER IN MY BOX

There's a Monster in my box

And he's got the chicken pox

He's purple with green dots

In my room!

There's a Monster wearing pants

As he does the chicken dance

While he dreams about romance

On the Moon!

Now, the Monster hums Fandango

When he does a little Tango

While munching on a mango

I swear it's true!

Then he sings a little Gospel

Dancing with some real soul

When it turns into some rock 'n' roll

I'll dance, too

# EVIL CLOWN BURGERS

Listen up, bad boys and girls
Come down to Greasy Burger Worlds

I'm your host, Evil Clown
Coming soon to your town

Eat rotten candy and oily cake,
There's nothing awful I can't bake

Have a burger, want some cheese?
I'll top it off with lots of greaze

Into the batch then I will toss
My very secret, slimy sauce

Would you like some fries with that?
Or maybe dirt with leg of bat?

Only 1 calorie, that's a fact,
Around here we don't count the fat

So what if you can't fit through the door
I'll butter you up, eat some more!

And when you get real juicy
At an abnormally large size
I'll dice you into pieces
And serve you in meat pies

I'll charge a dollar-fifty
They'll keep coming back for more
I'll make them eat till they get fat
And can't fit through the door

I'll psycho-hypnotize them
With my hypnotizing shake
Made with hoodoo-voodoo ice cream
And a poisonous live snake

It'll turn you into zombies
I'll control you with my words
And top you off with magic dust
To turn you into nerds

I'll force you up a mountain
You dumb ol' raff and riff
When at the top, I will command
"You all, jump off the cliff!"

If these things sound awful
And you're too scared to attend
I say, "Good riddance to you
I wouldn't serve you in the end"

For only snotty lazy-butts
Are accepted in my place
'Cuz goody-goody sandwiches
Just are not my taste

# MRS. PAT

Oh, ol' Mrs. Pat
is wearing her cat
as a stole when she walks
Down the lane

Mrs. Pat lost her noodle
And is wearing a poodle
On her head and I think
She's insane

With a purse of reptile
Genuine Crocodile
On her arm as I see her
Each day

The snake meant to cloak her
is starting to choke her
But still she is acting
Quite gay

I asked Mrs. Pat
Why is it that
Animals put up with
All that they do?

She said "Dey don't mind
'Cuz I treat 'em real kind!
I just wanted my own
Private zoo"

# LAST NIGHT I HAD A DREAM

How does the night fall
Does it fall at all?
It blocks the sun out
Like a shade

Are the stars just in my eyes
Or poked out of the skies
And will the lights
Up in Heaven just fade?

Last night I had a dream
Or so it did seem
That I floated to the sky
Like a cloud

And the Queen of the Night
Blocked out all the light
With her black velvet,
Satin-lined shroud

The stars sewn in her lining
All started shining
I swung back and forth
On their string

The stars fell like tears
Which washed away my fears
'Cuz they sounded like bells
When they ring

Then I got so elated
When electric beams pulsated
And created the Black Hole
I fell through

I was inter-dimensional
(Which, of course, is nonsensical)
But the world looked so different
And new

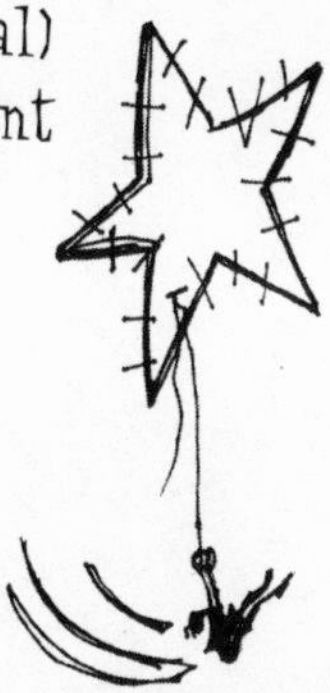

I could touch the universe
Which was created in reverse
And hung so thick
I felt like fainting

It stuck like glue to my clothes
From my head to my toes
Till I realized that I
Was in my painting

I held on to the galaxy
And steadied on the Milky Way
As I leaned out of the picture
With my head

When I saw my cozy room
I let go, and fell then
"BOOM"
Right into my own
Comfy Bed

# X-Q31

For Christmas '99
The hottest brand of toy
Was the X-Q31,
A friend for girl or boy

The commercials say,
"It moves and walks,
It cleans your house,
It even talks!"

So, every child asked for one
On their Christmas lists
To have a friend they can control,
Is every child's wish

Christmas morning
They awoke with glee
To find him standing
Beneath their tree

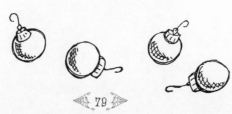

They played for days
With X-Q31
Dancing, Prancing,
And having fun

He whipped their rooms
All into shape,
And then he baked them
A chocolate cake!

On New Year's Eve
They had him serve,
Champagne and
Fancy, odd hors d'oeuvres

Then just at twelve
The year two thousand
The robots started
Freaking out, and...

Guests watched the robots
As they smashed
Every New
Millennium Glass

They tore up rooms
Acting bonkers,
Around the world
From Tibet to Yonkers

Then they proceeded
To destroy
Every brand new
Christmas toy

That was an awful,
Dreadful night.
Those robots put up
Quite a fight.

But when it was over
A recall was done,
And a rebate was
Mailed to everyone.

With a note attached
From the company,
"Accept our apology
And this money."

It's no wonder
The robots went berserk.
Why the remote controls
Wouldn't work

For these robots,
Who were defiant
Were not
Y2K compliant.

# JIM WON'T GO TO BED

Little Jim won't go to bed
After he's been bathed and fed

"I need water, I need to pee,
How 'bout a story? Read to me!"

But his Mom and Dad just said,
"Quiet down and go to bed!"

They'd turn out the light
And say, "It'll be alright"

And Jim would pull up the sheet
Afraid of the monsters he'd meet

They'd come out one-slimy one by one
Because the party had just begun

There's the monster in the closet
Who doesn't like the light
But, when it's dark
He starts to bark
It can give you quite a fright!

And that Slimy Sliverdoodle
She's hiding underneath the bed
With a certain
Tagley Wangley
I think his name is Fred

Underneath the floorboards
Lives weird Abercrombie
With hypnotic eyes
I now realize
That I am his zombie

The fiends that share the toy chest
Are in a band called Psychopation
They start to rockin'
Mom starts to knockin'
And says, "You'll wake the nation!"

She never will quite understand
Why I can never sleep
"Instead of creatures
With awful features
Can't you just count sheep?"

# THE DINER

Tonight I went into 'The Diner'
It gave me quite the creeps
It smelled like burning pumpkins
And the customers were freaks!

Some had spider toupees
Others, technicolored eyes
And still some other patrons
Had rolly, polly thighs

Squeezed into their tiny seats
Gobbling livers and gook
Prepared down in the cellar
By a gourmet, cannibal cook

A bloody rare steak
Was the Cook's special dish
And I saw a man eating
A man-eating fish!

When the waitress took my order
I looked up to say "Pancakes"
Then saw her fine from head to toe
But her hair was made out of snakes

Hair all made out of snakes?

Her hair was made out of snakes!

Wild and Wiggly
Slimy and Sliggly
Hair all made out of snakes

I hollered and callered
But she just followed with
"Hey Kid, that's just the breaks."

# EDGAR: THE INVISIBLE KID

Edgar was not REALLY invisible.

Not at first, at least.

It happened quite slowly.

Like a good stew or pot roast, he needed awhile to simmer before he became 100 percent, absolutely, positively invisible.

Edgar was given as a small child to the richest people in town, the Frunks. But all the wealth in the world could not make them a likable family.

The father of the clan was a stern, aging business man, who had spent a majority of his years in the stock market.

Buying and selling.        Trying and yelling.

Five days a week, except on weekends when he would worry about work while chewing on his cigar and reading the newspaper.

The mother that followed was a perfect "business man's wife." She knew the appropriate time and place for everything. Keeping up appearances was her goal in life, although behind closed doors, she's was a bitter and petty woman. Obsessed only with money and her dying beauty.

This 'appropriate' couple had created two children of their very own. Twins to be precise. Two of the loveliest angels. Long, flowing blonde locks framed their crystal blue eyes, which captured the onlooker in a hypnotic state.

Unfortunately, their outer beauty did not match the ugliness that they had inside them. Their years of primping had made them shallow. And since their parents had always given them everything they wanted, they became selfish, spoiled brats. Blaming everything on other people and crying at the very mention of the word "No."

They were very hard to get along with, but since they had each other, they had very little purpose for anyone else. They shared a deep connection, which enabled them to speak to each other in thought. This was very unnerving for anyone present, for it was never known if something awful was being said about the third party without them knowing it.

Edgar thought they were freaky!

He thought the whole family was freaky!

The morning he had first met Mrs. Frunk, Edgar's mother had been crying. She had no money and could not afford to feed Edgar, much less herself. She had met a woman, a Mrs. Frunk, who was picnicking in a park in the 'good' part of town. His mother pleaded for some scraps of food.

But Mrs. Frunk was a stern and uncaring woman.

She told Edgar's mother that she would only give her food in exchange for Edgar. She had been unsuccessful in giving her husband a son and knew that Mr. Frunk would very much enjoy getting one for his Birthday present.

Edgar's mother was a good mother and knew that she could not feed and take care of him as well as this wealthy woman. It broke her heart to give him up, but understood that it was best for Edgar. She agreed and Mrs. Frunk took Edgar away... crying.

Edgar had to hide for two days in Mrs. Frunk's closet to avoid ruining Mr. Frunk's birthday surprise. Mrs. Frunk brought him enormous meals, with special desserts, like cheesecake and apple fritters. Edgar ate every morsel as if he had not eaten in days, which he had not.

Mrs. Frunk said, "My dear boy, we must get you fattened up in time for Mr. Frunk's party. We can't have him opening up his present, only to find a skeleton inside."

Edgar thought the large meals were heavenly. But, when he was finished, Mrs. Frunk would turn out the light and close the closet door. It would be so dark that Edgar couldn't even see his own hand and he would cry and dream of his mother. His real mother.

On Mr. Frunk's birthday, Edgar was put in a box, which was wrapped in hand-made Italian paper and tied with a blue silk ribbon. Mr. Frunk was much too busy to open his presents immediately and insisted on eating his special

Birthday dinner and cake first. Edgar waited patiently, not even moving a muscle when his nose itched.

Finally, after eating every crumb on the table, Mr. Frunk sat back in his chair, burped and announced that he would now receive his presents. He got a new silk power tie, an expensive watch, three cigars from Cuba and a gold-plated pocket calculator.

At last, Mrs. Frunk announced that she "Had saved the best for last!" She laid the fancy, blue ribbon tied package in front of Mr. Frunk. He hummed and hawed about the best way to open his present until he opted to just rip into it. When he opened the lid, he stared in long silence and sat back in his chair.

"It's a new son, Honey," Mrs. Frunk squeaked. "I knew you always wanted one!"

"Uhuh." Mr. Frunk cleared his throat. "Thank you, Bunny. Tell me son, what's 31 times 17?" he barked at Edgar in a rough and gravely voice.

"Um, I don't know, sir." Edgar managed to cry out.

This infuriated Mr. Frunk. "What do you mean, you don't know? What grade are you in? Are you stupid or something? Answer me boy! Speak up!"

"I'm not in any grade, sir" Edgar replied. His mother had tried to enroll him in school, but since she could not afford tuition, books or school clothes, no school would accept him.

"Well, tomorrow you go to school. A boy must know things like what 31 times 17 is. Now go to bed!" Mr. Frunk yelled. He was already disappointed in his new son.

Meanwhile, the twins sat in utter amazement.

They had not agreed to this new addition to their family.
And they did not approve. Worst of all, Edgar was cute.
They had always been the cute ones in the family and
this was very much a threat to them. Father worked all
the time, so they barely got to spend any time with him
as it was. They loved it when father got home from work.
He would set them on his lap, give them money and toys
and then send them on their way. 'Did this mean that
Edgar would get the toys and money now?' they thought.

They silently made a pact with each other to make
Edgar's life with the Frunks as miserable as possible.

Edgar went to his room.

Although at first he thought his room was in Mrs. Frunk's closet, he was quickly re-directed to a small room behind the kitchen. It had no windows, but the ceiling had a crack in it that revealed light coming from Mr. and Mrs. Frunk's upstairs bedroom. It was cold and Edgar longed for the warm embrace of his mother. His real mother.

The next morning, Mr. Frunk abruptly interrupted Edgar's dream by charging into his room at 4 a.m. He was having a delicious dream about flying in the flowing fabrics of his mother's apron, while she sang his favorite lullaby to him.

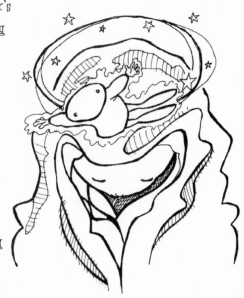

The wind whistled in time to her song and lifted him higher and higher until he circled her head so fast that he appeared as a glowing halo shining light upon an angel's brow.

But, it quickly
faded as his eyes
sprang open to see the
chubby face of Mr.
Frunk yelling, "Get up
kid. Time for school!"

The Frunks had not
had time to get new
school clothes for Edgar,
but had promised the principal that tomorrow he would
be more suitably dressed. The other school children made a
mockery of Edgar. They jeered at his clothes and made
fun of how much smaller he was then everyone else.

The teacher made him sit in the back of the classroom

to avoid offending the other
students. All during the day,
the other kids turned
around in their seats and
made horrid faces at Edgar.
But, he tried his best to
just ignore them and listen
to the teacher. He had to
find out what 31 times 17
was before the day was over.

At recess Edgar sat by himself on the steps of the school. That is, until the twins came and sat on either side of him.

"Well, well. What do we have here, Betty?"
"Looks like a little bitty mouse to me, Hetty."
"Looks more like a rat to me."

Then they laughed and laughed and laughed and laughed.

And they laughed some more as they skipped away to play on the swings.

Edgar sat in silence. He almost chocked himself trying not to cry. But, one single tear slipped out and fell onto his shoe, making it actually look shiny. He was lonesome for his mother.

When he got back to the Frunk's
house after school, the twins had already
come home. They had broken a vase and
told their mother that they had seen
Edgar break it. By the time Mr. Frunk
got home, the twins had managed to
break two more vases, shave the cat and
hide a pair of their father's best cuff
links. All this they blamed on Edgar.

He was sent to his room without supper.

It wasn't a big deal for Edgar to not have supper. He
didn't normally have much to eat anyway. But, since the
Frunks had not allowed him to eat breakfast and had not
given him a lunch either, Edgar's tummy started to growl. He
laid on his cold bed and listened to the song in his stomach
until it sounded like a lullaby. He drifted off to sleep.

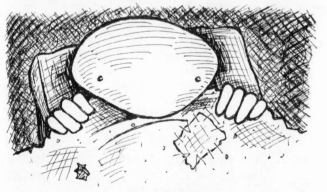

On this night, his dreams were dark.

He was in a train station with grey clouds of smoke encircling his head. In the distance he could see his mother walking. He tried to yell to her, but when he opened his mouth, no sound would come out. She walked further away from him. He started to run towards her, but the smoke turned into a cyclone which lifted him high into the sky.

The next day he was given new school clothes, even though the Frunks were very displeased with him. The clothes were too big and very scratchy. Edgar hated wearing them. It was as if he was wearing clothes that belonged to someone else.

His new duds did not change the way the other school children felt about him. They still stared and made faces and shot spitballs at his head. The twins still called him names and blamed 'accidents' on him. The teacher would not even say his name at roll call and would never let him ask any questions.

Later, at suppertime, nobody called for Edgar to come eat. When he left his room to see what the delicious smells were, he noticed that the dining room table was only set for four and exactly four family members were stuffing their faces.

Edgar went back to his room hungry, again.

That marked the beginning of Edgar's' invisibility.

He would sneak into the kitchen when the others had
gone to bed. There were never any leftovers, but Edgar
was quite content eating cold cereal or a piece of fresh
fruit. It was all delicious to him and it kept his tummy
from growling, so he could get some sleep.

He felt guilty taking food without asking. He had not
been made to feel like he was a welcomed part of the
Frunk's household. He felt more like a mouse, just like the
twins had called him. But as long as he was out of sight,
the Frunks would not scold him. And Edgar realized that
only he could take care of himself.

The next morning, nobody woke Edgar for school. He woke up late, threw on his new scratchy clothes and ran all the way there. His teacher did not even look up when he entered the classroom. None of the students turned to stare and throw spitballs at him. The twins did not call him names during recess. It was as if he did not even exist.

For over a month after that day, not a single soul uttered a single word to Edgar. Not a 'hello',

or a 'goodbye'

or even a disapproving grunt.

Edgar rather preferred it that way. He fed himself at night and listened intently to the teacher during the day. Not only did he learn what 31 times 17 was, but many other multiplication problems as well. He learned how to read and write and excelled in his art class. He could answer any question the teacher asked, although she would never call on him when he raised his hand.

"No mind," thought Edgar. "At least no one is saying nasty things to me."

One night, Edgar strolled home at his own lonely pace. The moon was already out and the town clock struck 10 'o clock. Edgar had wanted to taste his new found freedom.

Since becoming invisible, he could go and do just about anything he wanted to do. He climbed the Main Street Park statue of Jeremiah Wainwright, the town hero. Nobody saw him. He picked apples off of Old Lady Petterman's tree. Nobody saw him. He visited the movie theater three times without paying and snuck into the projection booth, curious to know how the movies worked. Nobody saw him. He even, as scandalous as this might sound, ran naked through the church on St. Cloud Street.

But, still nobody saw him. Nobody ever saw him.

Edgar was convinced that he was invisible. There could be no other explanation.

But, just when he past The Soda Shoppe, he heard a slight sound. It sounded like his name. Edgar stopped in his tracks. It sounded so real, but he eventually brushed it off as being the wind.

## "Edgar"

There it was again. Edgar stopped and listened. Maybe he had become visible again. Maybe the mean kids at school were coming after him. Or the twins. Or Mr. and Mrs. Frunk!

He heard footsteps. Edgar ran. As fast as his little legs would carry him. He ran through the park, over the bridge and into the Community Garden. The footsteps continued,

getting
faster and
faster on
his trail.
They were
gaining on
him and he
could hear
his name
being
called. Over
and over
again.

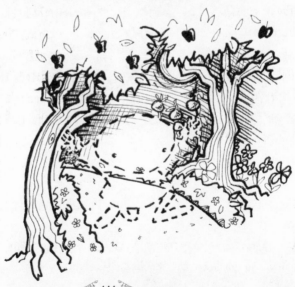

Finally when his little lungs felt as if they could explode, mysterious hands grabbed him from behind. These were the first hands to touch him in over a month. Their touch sent a tingle through Edgar's spine. Not like when the Frunks had touched him, though. Their hands were cold and clammy. These hands were warm and gentle.

Edgar swung around to see his captor and suddenly realized it was his mother. His real mother!

His eyes filled with tears as he grabbed on to his mothers waist. He felt his body get warm as his mother held him as close as she could. A rosy shine came over Edgar's cheeks and a twinkle from the moon shone bright in his eyes like a star on Earth. His arms filled with the color of fresh peaches while he was lifted up to his mother's bosom. As they embraced, Edgar once again became 100 percent, absolutely, positively visible.

And from that day forward,

Edgar never, ever became invisible again.

# GADZOOK'S LAGOON CREATURE

By the light
Of a Louisiana moon

Lives the old Creature
Of Gadzook's Lagoon

I read about him in
The Times Picayune

The first ever creature
To play the bassoon

Although he won't always
Play it in tune

You can see him perform
Down at Sid's Saloon

That wacky old Creature
From Gadzook's Lagoon

# Madame M

## ABOUT THE AUTHOR

Writer/Illustrator, Madame M is the "Mistress of The Creepy Little Things." She keeps them in her lovely basement, turned rec-room, to keep them from disturbing small children at night. Madame M married her 'love at first fright,' Wolfman Joe, who also is kept in the basement to avoid "accidents." Her favorite past-times are contacting the dead, creating love potions, attending the annual Creepy Little ScareFest and writing about her creepy little fiends.

# SWEET DREAMS, DAHLINGS!

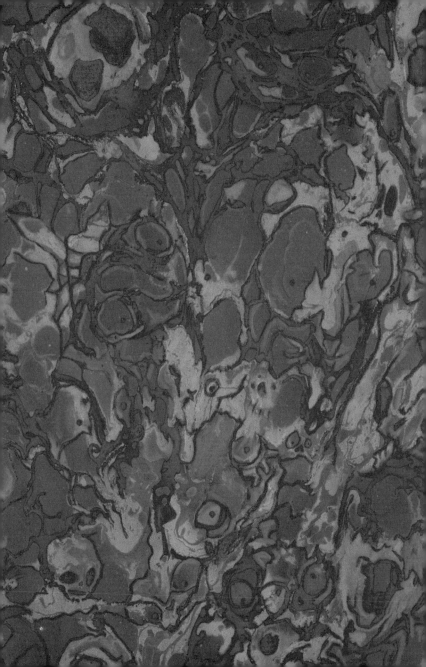